101 HITS FOR BUSKERS

BOOK 2 · PIANO/ORGAN EDITION WITH GUITAR CHORDS

Wise Publications
London/New York/Sydney/Cologne

Exclusive distributors:
Music Sales Limited,
8/9 Frith Street, London, W1V 5TZ, England.
Music Sales Pty. Limited,
120 Rothschild Avenue, Rosebery, NSW 2018, Australia.

This book © Copyright 1978 by
Wise Publications
ISBN 0.86001.447.9
AM 19803

Designer: Howard Brown
Cover illustration: Michael Farrell

Music Sales complete catalogue lists thousands
of titles and is free from your local music
book shop, or direct from Music Sales Limited.
Please send £1.75 (cheque) for postage to
Music Sales Limited. 8/9 Frith Street, London W1V 5TZ

Printed and bound in Great Britain by
Scotprint Ltd, Musselburgh

Ain't She Sweet **1**
All You Need Is Love **2**
Amazing Grace **3**
And I Love Her **4**
Angelo **5**
Anniversary Song (Oh! How We Danced) **6**
Arrivederci Roma **7**
As Long As He Needs Me **8**
Auld Lang Syne **9**
'A' You're Adorable **11**
Ballad Of Bonnie And Clyde (The) **13**
Banks Of The Ohio **12**
Big Spender **14**
Black And White **15**
Brazil **17**
Burlington Bertie **18**
Bye Bye Baby **16**
Can't Get Used To Losing You **19**
Carolina Moon **20**
Catch A Falling Star **21**
Chanson D'Amour **22**
Cielito Lindo **23**
Dancing Queen **24**
Danny Boy **25**
Darlin' **26**
England Swings **27**
Every Day **28**
Georgia On My Mind **30**
Get Back **31**
Girl Of My Dreams **29**
God Save The Queen **10**
Goodnight Sweetheart **32**
Granada **34**
Green Green Grass Of Home **33**
Guantanamera **35**
Happy Days Are Here Again **37**
He's Got The Whole World In His Hands **36**
Hey Jude **38**
Honeysuckle Rose **39**
I Believe **40**
I Can See Clearly Now **41**
I Can't Give You Anything But Love **42**
I Left My Heart In San Francisco **45**
I Wan'na Be Like You **49**
I (Who Have Nothing) **50**
If I Had A Hammer **44**
If You Know What I Mean **46**
I'll Walk With God **47**
It's Four In The Morning **43**
Jeannie With The Light Brown Hair **48**
King Of The Road **51**

Kiss Me Honey Honey Kiss Me **52**
Knowing Me, Knowing You **53**
Last Thing On My Mind (The) **54**
Lazy River **55**
Little Bit More (A) **56**
Live And Let Die **58**
Liverpool Lou **57**
Long and Winding Road (The) **59**
Love Me Tender **60**
Love's Been Good To Me **61**
Memories Are Made Of This **62**
Michelle **63**
Money Money Money **65**
Mood Indigo **64**
Mr. Tambourine Man **66**
Music Goes Round And Around (The) **67**
My Ding-A-Ling **68**
My Love **69**
Nights In White Satin **70**
On The Sunny Side Of The Street **71**
Paperback Writer **72**
Pennies From Heaven **73**
Quando Quando Quando **74**
Red Roses For A Blue Lady **75**
Release Me **76**
Sailing **77**
Save The Last Dance For Me **78**
Save Your Kisses For Me **79**
She **80**
Show Me The Way To Go Home **81**
Side By Side **83**
Sing **82**
Solitaire **84**
Sophisticated Lady **85**
Spinning Wheel **87**
Sugar Sugar **86**
Supercalifragilisticexpialidocious **88**
Superstar **89**
There Goes My Everything **90**
Try A Little Tenderness **91**
Tulips From Amsterdam **92**
Tuxedo Junction **93**
When I'm Sixty-Four **95**
When The Saints Go Marching In **94**
Why **98**
With A Little Help From My Friends **96**
You Are My Sunshine **99**
You Won't Find Another Fool Like Me **100**
You're A Star **97**
You're Nobody 'Til Somebody Loves You **101**

AIN'T SHE SWEET

Words by Jack Yellen
Music by Milton Ager

2
ALL YOU NEED IS LOVE

Words and Music by
John Lennon and Paul McCartney

AMAZING GRACE

Traditional
Adapted by Judy Collins

4
AND I LOVE HER

Words and Music by
John Lennon and Paul McCartney

Slowly and gently

I give her all my love, _ That's all I
She gives me ev'ry - thing, _ And ten - der -
Bright are the stars that shine, _ Dark is the

do, ___ And if you saw my love, _ You'd love her
ly, ___ The kiss my lov - er brings _ She brings to
sky. ___ I know this love of mine _ Will nev - er

too. _ I _ love her. _____ A love like ours _
me, _ And I love her. ____
die, _ And I love her. ____

___ could nev - er die. ___ As long as I _

___ have you near _ me.

___

5
ANGELO

Words and Music by
Tony Hiller, Les Sheridan and Martin Lee

Medium tempo

Long a-go, high on a moun-tain in Mex-i-co, lived a young shep-herd boy,

An-gel-o, who met a young girl and he loved her so. _____

Rich was she, came from a ve-ry high fam-i-ly, An-gel-o knew it could
Long a-go, high on a moun-tain in Mex-i-co, lived a young shep-herd boy,

nev-er be; they ran a-way to their des-ti-ny. _____
An-gel-o, who met a young girl and he loved her so. _____

Run-ning a-way_ to-geth-er, run-ning a-way_ for ev-er, An-gel-o. _____

Run-ning a-way_ from dan-ger, hid-ing from ev-'ry stran-ger, An-gel-o. _____

They knew it was-n't wrong,_they found a love so strong_they took their

lives that night, And in the morn-ing light_they found them on_ the sand,_they saw them

ly-ing there hand in hand. _____

ANNIVERSARY SONG
(OH! HOW WE DANCED)

Words and Music by
Al Jolson and Saul Chaplin

Valse moderato

Oh, how we danced on the night we were wed,
We vowed our true love, though a word wasn't said.
The world was in bloom, there were stars in the skies,
Except for the few that were there in your eyes.

night seemed to fade into blos-som-ing dawn,
The sun shone a-new, but the dance lin-gered on.
Could we but re-live that sweet mo-ment sub-lime
We'd find that our love is un-al-tered by

Dear, as I held you so close in my arms, An-gels were sing-ing a hymn to your charms, Two hearts gent-ly beat-ing were mur-mur-ing low, "My dar-ling, I love you so." The time.

ARRIVEDERCI ROMA

Words by Garinei and Giovannini
Music by Renato Rascel
English lyrics by Carl Sigman

8
AS LONG AS HE NEEDS ME

Words and Music by
Lionel Bart

9
AULD LANG SYNE

Traditional

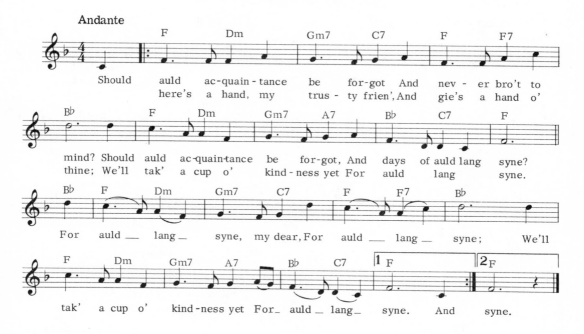

10
GOD SAVE THE QUEEN

Traditional

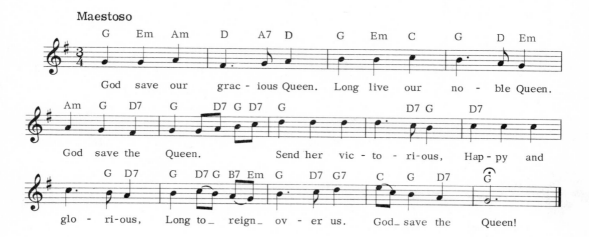

11
'A' YOU'RE ADORABLE

Words and Music by
Buddy Kaye, Fred Wise and Sidney Lippman

12
BANKS OF THE OHIO

Traditional.
Arranged by
Bruce Welch and John Farrar

13

THE BALLAD OF BONNIE AND CLYDE

Words and Music by
Mitch Murray and Peter Callander

BIG SPENDER

Words by Dorothy Fields
Music by Cy Coleman

Strong slowish beat

The min-ute you walked in the joint I could see you were a man of dis-tinc-tion, a real big spen-der,— Good look-ing,— so re-fined,— Say, would-n't you like to know what's go-ing on in my mind?— So let me get right to the point, I don't pop my cork for ev'-ry guy I see. Hey! Big spen-der,— Spend a lit-tle time— with me.

15

BLACK AND WHITE

Words by David Arkin
Music by Earl Robinson

1. The ink is black, The page is white, To-geth-er we learn to read and write, To read and write. And now a child can un-der-stand This is the law of all the land, All the land! The ink is black, The page is white, To-geth-er we learn to read and write, To read and write.

2. The

2. The slate is black, the chalk is white,
The words stand out so clear and bright,
So clear and bright.
And now at last we plainly see
The alphabet of liberty, Liberty!
The slate is black, the chalk is white,
The words stand out so clear and bright,
So clear and bright.

3. A child is black, a child is white,
The whole world looks upon the sight,
A beautiful sight.
For very well the whole world knows
This is the way that freedom grows,
Freedom grows!
A child is black, a child is white,
The whole world looks upon the sight,
A beautiful sight.

4. The world is black, the world is white,
It turns by day and then by night,
It turns by night.
It turns so each and ev'ryone
Can take his station in the sun, in the sun!
The world is black, the world is white,
It turns by day and then by night,
It turns by night.

5. Their robes were black, their heads were white,
The schoolhouse doors were closed so tight,
Were closed up tight!
Nine judges all set down their names
To end the years and years of shame,
Years of shame!
The robes were black, the heads were white,
The schoolhouse doors were closed so tight,
Were closed up tight!

BYE BYE BABY

Words by Leo Robin
Music by Jule Styne

17
BRAZIL

Words by S. K. Russell
Music by Ary Barroso

18

BURLINGTON BERTIE

Words and Music by
William Hargreaves

Tempo di valse

1. I'm Bert, _____ p'raps you've heard of me; Bert, _____ you've had word of me; Jog-ging a - long, heart-y and strong, liv-ing on plates of fresh air. _____ I dress _____ up in fash-ion, and when I am feel-ing de - pressed, _____ I shave from my cuff all the whis-kers and fluff, stick my hat on and tod-dle up West. _____

Chorus

I'm Bur-ling-ton Ber-tie, I rise at ten thir-ty and saun-ter a - long like a toff. _____ I walk down the Strand with my gloves on my hand, then I walk down a - gain with them off. _____ I'm all airs and gra-ces, cor-rect ea-sy pa-ces, with-out food so

long I've for - got where my face is; I'm Bert, Bert, I have-n't a shirt, but my peo-ple are well off, you know! ____ Near-ly ev-'ry-one knows me, from Smith to Lord Rose-b'ry, I'm Bur-ling-ton Ber-tie from Bow! ____

2. I stroll with Lord Hurlington, roll in the Burlington,
    Call for champagne, walk out again, come back and borrow the ink.
    I live most expensive; like Tom Lipton, I'm in the swim.
    He's got so much 'oof' that he sleeps on the roof, and I live in the room over him.
        I'm Burlington Bertie, I rise at ten thirty then saunter along Temple Bar.
        As round there I skip I keep shouting, "Pip! Pip!", and the darn'd fools think I'm in my car.
        At Rothchild's I swank it, my body I plank it on his front doorstep with 'The Mail'
                                                                    for a blanket;
        I'm Bert, Bert, and Rothchild was hurt; he said, "You can't sleep there." I said, "Oh!"
    He said, "I'm Rothchild, sonny!" I said, "That's damn'd funny,
    I'm Burlington Bertie from Bow!"

3. I smile condescendingly while they're extending me
    Cheer upon cheer when I appear captain with my polo team.
    So strict are my people, they're William the Conqueror's strain.
    If they ever knew I'd been talking to you, why, they'd never look at me again!
        I'm Burlington Bertie, I rise at ten thirty and reach Kempton Park about three.
        I stand by the rail when a horse is for sale, and you ought to see Wooton watch me!
        I lean on some awning while Lord Derby's yawning, then he bids, "Two thousand,"
                                                                    and I bid, "Good morning;"
        I'm Bert, Bert, I'd buy one, a cert, but where could I keep it, you know!
    I can't let my man see me in bed with a gee-gee!
    I'm Burlington Bertie from Bow!

4. My pose, though ironical, shows that my monocle
    Holds up my face, keeps it in place, stops it from slipping away.
    Cigars, I smoke thousands; I usually deal in the Strand,
    But you've got to take care, when you're getting them there, or some idiot might stand
                                                                    on your hand.
        I'm Burlington Bertie, I rise at ten thirty then Buckingham Palace I view.
        I stand in the Yard while they're changing the guard, and the King shouts across, "Toodle-oo!"
        The Prince of Wales' brother, along with some other, slaps me on the back and says,
                                                                    "Come and see mother."
        I'm Bert, Bert, and royalty's hurt when they ask me to dine I say, "No.
    I've just had a banana with Lady Diana;
    I'm Burlington Bertie from Bow!"

19
CAN'T GET USED TO LOSING YOU

Words and Music by
Doc Pomus and Mort Shuman

Moderato

Guess there's no use in hang-in' round,   Guess I'll get dress'd and do the
Called up some girl I used to know,   Af - ter I heard her say hel -
I'll find some-bo - dy, wait and see.   Who am I kid - din'? On - ly

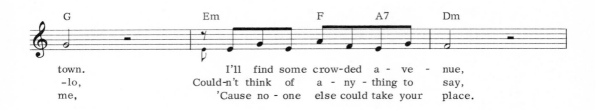

town.   I'll find some crow-ded a - ve - nue,
-lo,   Could-n't think of a - ny - thing to say,
me,   'Cause no - one else could take your place.

Tho' it will be emp-ty with-out you.
Since you're gone it hap-pens ev-'ry day.   Can't get used to los-in' you, no
Guess that I am just a hope-less case.

mat-ter what I try to do;   Gon - na live my whole life through   Lov-in' you. —

20
CAROLINA MOON

Words and Music by
Benny Davis and Joe Burke

CATCH A FALLING STAR

Words and Music by
Paul Vance and Lee Pockriss

Catch a fall-ing star and put it in your pock-et, Nev-er let it fade a-

-way. Catch a fall-ing star and put it in your pock-et,

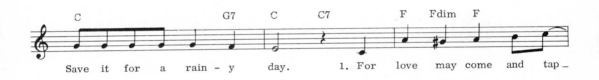

Save it for a rain-y day. 1. For love may come and tap

you on the shoul-der Some star-less night. And

just in case you feel you want to hold her, You'll have a pock-

-et full of star-light. Catch a fall-ing star and put it in your pock-et,

Nev - er let it fade a - way. Catch a fall - ing star and

put it in your pock - et, Save it for a rain - y day. 2. For

when your trou - bles start in mul - ti - ply - ing, And they just

might. It's ea - sy to for - get them with - out try - ing,

With just a pock - et full of star - light. Catch a fall - ing star and

put it in your pock - et, Nev - er let it fade a - way.

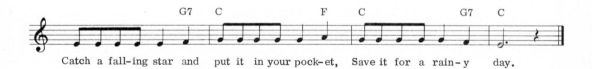

Catch a fall - ing star and put it in your pock - et, Save it for a rain - y day.

CHANSON D'AMOUR

Words and Music by
Wayne Shanklin

23
CIELITO LINDO

Words and Music by
Quirino Mendoza

24
DANCING QUEEN

Words and Music by
Benny Andersson, Stig Anderson and Bjorn Ulvaeus

Moderato

You can dance, — you can jive _____ hav-ing— the time of — your

life. — Oh _____ see that — girl, ___ watch that — scene, — dig in the

Danc-ing— Queen.

Fri-day night. and the lights are low, ____ look-ing out — for a

place to go. _____ Oh _____ where they play— the right mu-sic,

get-ting in the swing you come to look for a king. ___

An - y-bo - dy could be that guy, — night is young— and the
You're a tea - ser, you turn 'em on, _____ leave 'em burn-ing and

mu-sic's high, _____ with a bit — of rock mu-sic eve-ry-thing-is fine,
then you're gone _____ look-ing out — for an - oth-er, an - y-one — will do,

DANNY BOY

Traditional
Words by
Fred E. Weatherley

DARLIN'

Words and Music by
Brian Wilson and Mike Love

You know if words could say__ That dar-ling I'd
I was living like half a man__ Then I couldn't love but

find a-way__ To let you know what you meant to me_____
now I can__ You pick me up when I'm feel-ing sad_____

Guess it was meant to be_____ I hold you in my heart__
More so than I ev-er had_____ Gonna love you every sing-le night__

As life's most prec-ious part__ Oh,_____
'Cause I think you're too out of sight__ Oh,_____

dar-lin'_____ I dream a-bout you of-ten my__ pretty girl yeah_____ I
dar-lin'_____ I dream a-bout you of-ten my__ pretty girl yeah_____ I

love the way you sof-ten my life with your love__ your prec-ious love uh huh__
love the way you sof-ten my life with your love__ your prec-ious love uh huh__

1.
2.

D.S. and fade ad lib

Oh

ENGLAND SWINGS

Words and Music by
Roger Miller

28
EVERY DAY

Words and Music by
Norman Petty and Charles Hardin

GIRL OF MY DREAMS

Lyric and Music by
Sunny Clapp

GEORGIA ON MY MIND

Words by Stuart Gorrell
Music by Hoagy Carmichael

GET BACK

Words and Music by
John Lennon and Paul McCartney

Very brightly

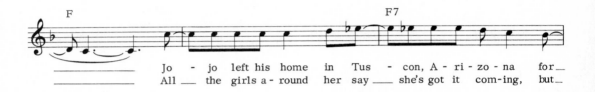

Jo - jo was a man who thought he was a lo - ner, but he knew it could - n't last.
Sweet Lo - ret - ta Mar - tin thought she was a wo - man, but she was an - oth - er man.

Jo - jo left his home in Tus - con, A - ri - zo - na for
All the girls a - round her say she's got it com - ing, but

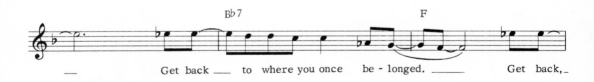

some Ca - li - for - nia grass. Get back, get back,
she gets it while she can.

Get back to where you once be - longed. Get back,

get back, Get back to where you once be - longed.

32
GOODNIGHT SWEETHEART

Words and Music by
Ray Noble, Jimmy Campbell and Reg Connelly

Moderato, con espressione

Good-night, sweet-heart, all my pray'rs are for you. Good-night, sweet-heart, I'll be watch-ing o'er you. Tears and part-ing may make us for-lorn, __ But with the dawn __ a new day is born, __ So I'll say Good-night, sweet-heart, sleep will ba-nish sor - row. Good-night, sweet-heart, till we meet to - mor - row.

Dreams en - fold you, in them, dear, I'll hold you.
(2) All your sad - ness soon will turn to glad-ness.
(3) Don't be blue, dear, dreams will all come true, dear.

Good - night, sweet-heart, good - night. ___

GREEN GREEN GRASS OF HOME

Words and Music by
Curly Putman

Moderato

The old home town looks the same As I step down from the
old house is still stand-ing, Tho' the paint is cracked and

train, And there to meet me is my ma-ma and pa-pa;
dry, And there's that old oak tree that I used to play on;

Down the road I look, and there runs Ma-ry,
Down the lane I walk with my sweet Ma-ry, Hair of gold and

Chorus

lips like cher-ries; It's good to touch the green, green grass of home.

1 & 2. Yes, they'll
3. Yes, they'll

1,2

all come to meet me, Arms reach-ing, smil-ing sweet-ly; It's
all come to see me In the

good to touch the green, green grass of home. 2. The shade of that

3

old oak tree As they lay me 'neath the green, green grass of home.

rall.

3. [spoken] Then I awake and look around me
At four grey walls that surround me,
And I realize that I was only dreaming,
For there's a guard and there's a sad old padre—
arm in arm we'll walk at daybreak;
Again I'll touch the green, green grass of home. [CHORUS]

34

GRANADA

Words by Dorothy Dodd
Music by Agustin Lara

GUANTANAMERA

Words by Jose Marti
Music adaptation by Hector Angulo and Pete Seeger

Moderato

Guan-ta-na-me-ra gua-ji-ra Guan-ta-na-me-ra

Guan-ta-na-me - ra gua-ji-ra Guan-ta-na-me - ra! ra!

1. Yo soy un hom-bre sin-ce-ro De don-de cre-ce la pal-ma.

Yo soy un hom-bre sin-ce-ro De don-de cre - ce la

pal-ma. Y antes de mo-rir-me quie - ro E-char mis ver-sos del al - ma.

2. Mi verso es de un verde claro,
Y de un carmin encendido.
Mi verso es de un verde claro,
Y de un carmin encendido.
Mi verso es un cierro herido
Que busca en el monte amparo.
[Chorus]

3. Con los pobres de la tierra
Quiero yo mi suerte echar.
Con los pobres de la tierra
Quiero yo mi suerte echar.
El arroyo de la sierra
Me complace mas que el mar.
[Chorus]

Literal translation:

1. I am a truthful man from the land
of palm trees.
Before dying I want to share these
poems of my soul.

2. My poems are light green,
but they are also flaming crimson.
My verses are like a wounded faun
seeking refuge in the forest.

3. With the poor people of this earth
I want to share my fate.
The little streams of the mountains
please me more than the sea.

HE'S GOT THE WHOLE WORLD IN HIS HANDS

Traditional

HAPPY DAYS ARE HERE AGAIN

Words by Jack Yellen
Music by Milton Ager

Allegro moderato

So long, sad times! Go 'long, bad times!
No more sigh-ing, No more cry-ing,

We are rid of you at last.
Clouds of grey have turned to blue.

How - dy, gay times! Clou - dy grey times,
Sor - row fly - ing, Cares de - ny - ing,

You are now a thing of the past. _____
All our ro - sy dreams have come true . _____ 'Cause

Hap - py days _ are here a - gain! _ The skies a - bove_

_ are clear a - gain. _ Let us sing a song _ of

HEY JUDE

Words and Music by
John Lennon and Paul McCartney

39
HONEYSUCKLE ROSE

Words by Andy Razaf
Music by Thomas Waller

I BELIEVE

Words and Music by
Ervin Drake, Irvin Graham, Jimmy Shirl and Al Stillman

I CAN SEE CLEARLY NOW

Words and Music by
Johnny Nash

Moderato, with a strong beat

I can see clear - ly now, the rain has gone.

I can see all ob - sta - cles in my way.

Gone are the dark clouds that had me blind,

It's gon - na be a bright, bright sun-shi-ny day,

It's gon - na be a bright, bright sun-shi-ny day.

I think I can make it now, the pain has gone.

All of the bad ___ feel-ings have dis-ap-peared, ___

Here is the rain - bow I've ___ been pray - ing for, ___

It's gon-na be ___ a bright, bright ___ sun-shi-ny day, ___

Look all a - round, ___ there's no-thing but blue sky, ___

___ Look straight a - head, ___ no-thing but blue sky. ___

D.C. al ⊕

CODA

It's gon - na be a bright,

bright ___ sun - shi - ny day. ___

42
I CAN'T GIVE YOU ANYTHING BUT LOVE

Words by Dorothy Fields
Music by Jimmy McHugh

Andante con moto

Gee, but it's tough to be broke, kid, __ It's not a joke, kid, It's a curse;
Rome was-n't built in a day, kid, __ You have to pay, kid, For what you get,

Think that you ought to be know-ing, __ My luck is go - ing __ from bad to worse.
But I am will - ing to wait, dear, Your lit-tle mate, dear, __ will not for - get.

Who knows some day I will win too, I'll be-gin to reach my prime.
You have a life-time be-fore you, I'll a-dore you, come what may.

Now, tho' I see what our end is, __ All I can spend is just my time.
Please don't be blue for the pre-sent, __ When it's so plea-sant to hear you say,

Chorus

I can't give you an - y - thing but love, Ba - by,

That's the on - ly thing I've plen - ty of, Ba - by,

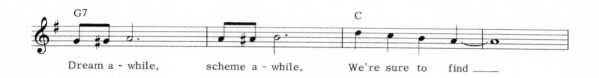

Dream a - while, scheme a - while, We're sure to find

hap-pi-ness, and I guess All those things you've al - ways pined for.

Gee, I'd like to see you look - ing swell, Ba - by,

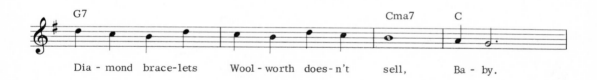

Dia - mond brace-lets Wool - worth does-n't sell, Ba - by.

Till that luck - y day, you know darned well, Ba - by.

I can't give you an - y - thing but love. love.

IT'S FOUR IN THE MORNING

Words and Music by
Jerry Chesnut

3. Last night I told her, this time it's all over,
   Making ten times I told her goodbye.
   Last night we broke up, this morning I woke up,
   And for the tenth time I'm changing my mind.
   I saw more love in her eyes when I left her
   Than most foolish men will ever see;
   And it's four in the morning, and once more the dawning
   Just woke up the wanting in me.

44
IF I HAD A HAMMER

Words and Music by
Lee Hays and Pete Seeger

45
I LEFT MY HEART IN SAN FRANCISCO

Words and Music by
Douglas Cross and George Cory

IF YOU KNOW WHAT I MEAN

Words and Music by
Neil Diamond

no-ther place, _ Do you re - mem-ber it babe?
no-ther place, _ Do you re - mem-ber it babe?

Chorus **Steady 4**

And the ra-di-o played like a car-ni-val tune as we lay in our bed in the oth - er

room, when we gave it a - way for the sake of a dream in a pen-ny ar - cade,

To Coda

If you know what I mean.

Verse
Tempo I

Here's to the songs we used to sing,

And here's to the times we used to know; _ It's hard to hold them in our

D.S. al

arms a - gain, and hard to let them go. _ Do you

CODA

If you know what I mean, If you know what I

mean, If you know what I mean.

47
I'LL WALK WITH GOD

Words by Paul Francis Webster
Music by Nicholas Brodszky

Moderato, molto espress.

I'll walk with God ___ from this day on,

His help-ing hand ___ I'll lean up-on. This is my prayer, ___

___ my hum-ble plea, ___ May the Lord be ev-er with me. ___

There is no death, ___ tho' eyes grow dim. There is no fear

when I'm near to Him. ___ I'll lean on Him for-

ev-er, And He'll for-sake me nev-er. ___

Cantabile, più mosso

He will not fail me as long _____ as my faith is

strong, _____ What - ev - er road I may walk a - long. _____

Tempo I

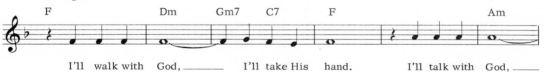

I'll walk with God, _____ I'll take His hand. I'll talk with God, _____

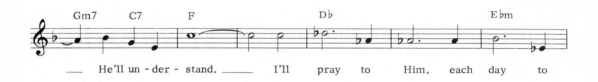

_____ He'll un - der - stand. _____ I'll pray to Him, each day to

Him, And He'll hear the words _____ that I say. _____ His

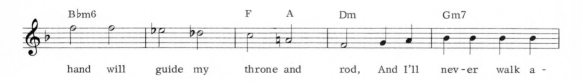

hand will guide my throne and rod, And I'll nev - er walk a -

Broadly

lone while I walk _____ with God! _____

JEANNIE WITH THE LIGHT BROWN HAIR

Words and Music by
Stephen Foster

I dream of Jean-nie with the light brown hair,
I long for Jean-nie with the day - dawn smile,

Borne, like a va - pour, on the sum-mer's air; I see her trip-ping where the
Rad - iant in glad-ness, warm with win-ning guile; I hear her mel-o- dies, like

bright streams play, Hap-py as the dai - sies that dance on her way.
joys gone by, Sigh-ing round my heart o'er the fond hopes that die;

Man -y were the wild notes her mer-ry voice would pour, Man -y were the blithe birds that
Sigh-ing like the night wind and sob-bing like the rain, Wail-ing for the lost one that

war - bled them o'er; Ah! I dream of Jean-nie with the
comes not a - gain; Ah! I long for Jean-nie and my

light brown hair, Float-ing, like a va-pour, on the soft sum-mer air.
heart bows low, Nev - er more to find her where the bright wa-ters flow.

49
I WAN'NA BE LIKE YOU

Words and Music by
Richard M. Sherman and Robert B. Sherman

50
I WHO HAVE NOTHING

English words by
Jerry Leiber and Mike Stoller
Music by C. Donida

KING OF THE ROAD

Words and Music by
Roger Miller

KISS ME HONEY HONEY

Words and Music by
Al Timothy and Michael Jullen

53
KNOWING ME, KNOWING YOU

Words and Music by
Benny Andersson, Stig Anderson and Bjorn Ulvaeus

Moderato

No more＿ care - free＿ laugh - ter, ＿＿＿＿
Mem- 'ries, ＿ good days, ＿ bad days ＿＿＿＿

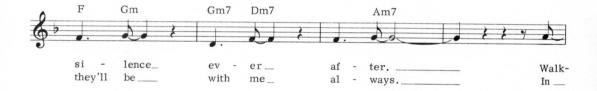

si - lence＿ ev - er＿ af - ter. ＿＿＿＿ Walk-
they'll be ＿＿ with me＿ al - ways. ＿＿＿＿ In ＿

- ing thro' an em-pty house,＿ tears in my eyes ;＿
＿＿ these old fa - mil-iar rooms ＿ chil-dren would play ;＿

This is where the sto - ry ends,＿ this is good-bye. ＿＿＿＿
Now there's on-ly em-pti - ness, ＿ no - thing to say. ＿＿＿＿

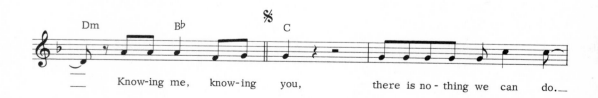

＿＿ Know-ing me, know-ing you, there is no-thing we can do.＿

54
THE LAST THING ON MY MIND

Words and Music by
Tom Paxton

55
LAZY RIVER

Words and Music by
Hoagy Carmichael and Sidney Arodin

56
A LITTLE BIT MORE

Words and Music by
Bobby Gosh

57
LIVERPOOL LOU

Words and Music by
Dominic Behan

58
LIVE AND LET DIE

Words and Music by
Paul McCartney

59

THE LONG AND WINDING ROAD

Words and Music by
John Lennon and Paul McCartney

60
LOVE ME TENDER

Words and Music by
Elvis Presley and Vera Matson

Moderately slow

1. Love me ten-der, love me sweet; Nev-er let me go.
2. Love me ten-der, love me long; Take me to your heart.
3. Love me ten-der, love me dear; Tell me you are mine.

[opt.] When at last my dreams come true, Dar-ling, this I know:

You have made my life com-plete, And I love you so.
For it's there that I be-long, And we'll nev-er part.
I'll be yours through all the years Till the end of time.
Hap-pi-ness will fol-low you Eve-ry-where you go.

Chorus

Love me ten-der, love me true; All my dreams ful-

fill. For, my dar-lin', I love you,

1, 2
And I al-ways will.

3 (and opt.)
And I al-ways will.

61
LOVE'S BEEN GOOD TO ME

Words and Music by
Rod McKuen

62
MEMORIES ARE MADE OF THIS

Words and Music by
Terry Gilkyson, Richard Dehr and Frank Miller

63

MICHELLE

Words and Music by
John Lennon and Paul McCartney

64
MOOD INDIGO

Words and Music by
Duke Ellington, Irving Mills and Albany Bigard

MONEY MONEY MONEY

Words and Music by
Benny Andersson and Bjorn Ulvaeus

Steady 4

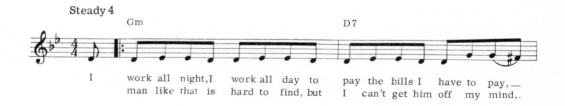

I work all night, I work all day to pay the bills I have to pay, —
man like that is hard to find, but I can't get him off my mind, —

ain't it sad; ____ And still there nev-er seems to be a
ain't it sad; ____ And if he hap-pens to be free I

sin-gle pen-ny left for me, ____ that's too bad. ____ —
bet he would-n't fan-cy me, ____ that's too bad. ____ So

In my dreams ___ I have a plan; ___ if I got me a
I must leave, ____ I'll have to go ___ to Las Ve-gas or

rit

weal-thy man, ___ I would-n't have to work at all. I'd
Mon-a-co ____ and win a for-tune in a game. My

MR. TAMBOURINE MAN

Words and Music by
Bob Dylan

Moderate 2

Hey! Mis-ter Tam-bou-rine Man, play a song for me, I'm not

sleep-y and there is no place I'm go-in' to. ____

Hey! Mis-ter Tam-bou-rine Man, play a song for me. In the

jin-gle jan-gle morn-in' I'll come fol-low-in' you. ____

Verse

Tho' I know that eve-nin's em-pire has re-turned in-to sand,

Van-ished from my hand, Left me blind-ly here to stand, but still not

sleep-in'. ____ My wear-i-ness a-maz-es me, I'm

brand-ed on my feet. I have no one to meet, And the

an-cient emp-ty street's too dead for dream-in'. ____

THE MUSIC GOES ROUND AND AROUND

Words by 'Red' Hodgson
Music by Edward Farley and Michael Riley

MY DING-A-LING

Words and Music by
Chuck Berry

Moderato

Verse 1

When I was a lit-tle bid-dy boy, My grand-mother bought me a cute lit-tle toy, —

Sil - ver bells hang-ing on a string, — She told me it was my ding-a-ling-a-ling. Oh

Chorus

My ding-a-ling, my ding-a-ling, I want you to play with my ding-a-ling,

My ding-a-ling, my ding-a-ling, I want you to play with my ding-a-ling. And

Verses 2, 3, 4, 5

then mom-ma took me to Gram-mar school, — But I stopped off in the

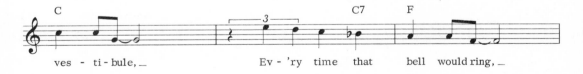

ves - ti-bule, — Ev - 'ry time that bell would ring, —

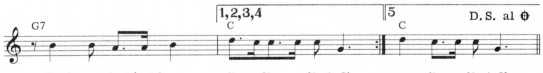

Catch me playin' with my ding-a-ling- a -ling! Oh own ding-a-ling! Oh

CODA

my ding-a-ling! Oh your ___ ding-a-ling, your ___ ding-a-ling, We saw ___

___ you playin' with your ___ ding-a-ling; Well my ___ ding-a-ling, ev -

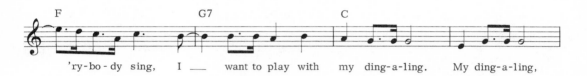

'ry-bo-dy sing, I ___ want to play with my ding-a-ling. My ding-a-ling,

my ding-a-ling, I want to play with my ding- a - ling!

3. Once I was climbing the garden wall,
   I slipped and had a terrible fall;
   I fell so hard I heard bells ring,
   But held on to my ding-a-ling-a-ling!
   [Chorus]

4. Once I was swimming 'cross Turtle Creek man,
   Them snappers all around my feet,
   Sure was hard swimming 'cross that thing
   With both hands holding my ding-a-ling-a-ling!
   [Chorus]

5. This here song it ain't so sad,
   The cutest little song you ever had.
   Those of you who will not sing
   You must be playing with your own ding-a-ling!
   [Chorus]

69
MY LOVE

Words and Music by
Paul and Linda McCartney

NIGHTS IN WHITE SATIN

Words and Music by
Justin Hayward

Slowly

Nights in white sa-tin ___ nev-er reach-ing the end,
Ga-zing at peo-ple, ___ some hand in hand,

Let-ters I've writ-ten, ___ nev-er mean-ing to send, ___
Just what I'm go-ing through they can't un-der-stand. ___

Beau-ty I'd al-ways missed with these eyes ___ be-fore, Just what the truth is ___
Some try to tell me ___ thoughts they can-not de-fend. Just what you want to be,

I can't say an-y-more, ___ 'cause I love you, ___ Yes, I ___ love you, ___ Oh, how ___ I
you'll be in the end, ___ and I love you, ___

love you. ___ How ___ I ___ love you.

D.S. al fine

71
ON THE SUNNY SIDE OF THE STREET

Words by Dorothy Fields
Music by Jimmy McHugh

PAPERBACK WRITER

Words and Music by
John Lennon and Paul McCartney

73
PENNIES FROM HEAVEN

Words by John Burke
Music by Arthur Johnston

QUANDO QUANDO QUANDO

Words by A. Testa
Music by Tony Renis
English lyrics by Pat Boone

RED ROSES FOR A BLUE LADY

Words and Music by
Sid Tepper and Roy Brodsky

Moderato

I want some red ros-es for a blue la-dy,

Mis-ter Flo-rist, take my or-der, please. _____ We

had a sil-ly quar-rel the oth-er day, _____

Hope these pret-ty flow-ers chase her blues a-way. _____ Wrap up some

red ros-es for a blue la-dy, Send them to the

sweet-est gal in town, _____ And if they do the

trick, I'll hur-ry back to pick Your best white or-chid

for her wed-ding gown. I want some gown. _____

76
RELEASE ME

Words and Music by
Eddie Miller, Dub Williams, Robert Young and Robert Harris

Moderato

1. Please re - lease me, let me go, _____ For I don't love you an - y - more. To waste our lives would be a sin. _____ Re - lease me and let me love a - gain.

2. I have found a new love dear, _____ And I will al - ways want her near. Her lips are warm while yours are cold. _____ Re - lease me, my dar - ling, let me go.

3. Please re - lease me, can't you see _____ You'd be a fool to cling to me? To live a lie would bring us pain, _____ So re - lease me and let me love a - gain. _____

SAILING

Words and Music by
Gavin Sutherland

Moderato

I am sail-ing, I am sail-ing home a - gain_ 'cross the sea. I am
fly - ing, I am fly-ing like a bird_ 'cross the sea. I am

sail-ing stor-my wa - ters, to be near_you, to be free. I am
fly - ing, pass-ing high clouds to be near_you, to be

free. Can you hear me, can you hear me thro' the dark_night, far a - way? I am

dy - ing,_ for ev-er try-ing to be with_you; who can say? Can you

hear_me, can you hear me thro' the dark_night, far a - way. I am
sail - ing, we are sail-ing home a - gain _ 'cross the sea. We are

dy - ing,_ for ev-er try-ing to be with_you; who can say?
sail-ing _ stor-my wa-ters, to be near_you, to be

Repeat and fade

We are free. Oh Lord to be near_you, to be free. Oh Lord to be

78
SAVE THE LAST DANCE FOR ME

Words and Music by
Doc Pomus and Mort Shuman

You can dance ev'ry dance with the guy who gave you the eye; let him
know that the mu-sic is fine, like spark-ling wine;— go and

hold you tight.— You can smile ev'ry smile for the man who
have your fun.— Laugh and sing, but while we're a-part — don't

held your hand — 'neath the pale moon-light.—
give your heart — to an-y-one. — But don't for-

get who's tak-ing you home, and in whose arms you're gon-na be.—

So dar-lin', — save the last dance for me. Oh, I

Ba-by, don't you know I love you so? — Can't you feel it when we touch?

I will nev-er, nev - er let you go. ___ I love you, oh so

much. You can dance, go and car - ry on ___ till the

night is gone ___ and it's time to go. ___ If he asks if you're

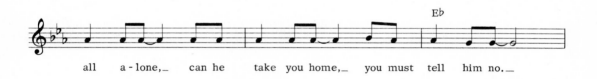

all a - lone, ___ can he take you home, ___ you must tell him no. ___

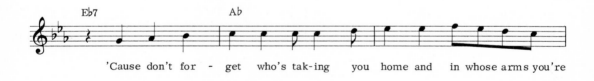

'Cause don't for - get who's tak-ing you home and in whose arms you're

gon - na be. ___ So, dar-lin', _____ save the

To Coda ✛   *D. S. al Coda* ✛ *CODA*

last dance for me. You can me. _____

79
SAVE YOUR KISSES FOR ME

Words and Music by
Tony Hiller, Lee Sheriden and Martin Lee

SHE

Words by Herbert Kretzmer
Music by Charles Aznavour

Moderato

She ____ may be the face I can't for - get, ____ a trace of plea-sure or re -

gret, ____ may be my trea-sure or the price I have to pay.

She __ may be the song that sum - mer sings, ____ may be the chill that aut - umn

brings, __ may be a hun-dred dif-fer-ent things__ with-in the mea-sure of a day.

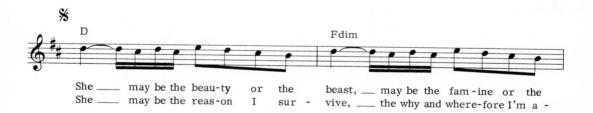

She ____ may be the beau-ty or the beast, ____ may be the fam - ine or the
She ____ may be the reas-on I sur-vive, ____ the why and where-fore I'm a -

feast, ____ may turn each day in - to a heav - en or a hell.
live, ____ the one I'll care for through the rough and read-y years,

She ___ may be the mir-ror of my dream, ___ a smile re-flec-ted in a
Me, ___ I'll take her laugh-ter and her tears ___ and make them all my sou-ven-

stream. ___ She may not be what she may seem in-side her shell.
irs, ___ For where she goes I've got to

She ___ who al-ways seems so hap-py in a crowd, whose eyes can be so pri-vate and so

proud; ___ no one's al-lowed to see them when they cry.

She ___ may be the love that can-not hope to last, ___ may come to me from sha-dows of the

past ___ that I re - mem-ber till the day I die. ___

be; The mean-ing of my life is she, ___ she mm she.

81
SHOW ME THE WAY TO GO HOME

Words and Music by
Irving King and Hal Swain

82
SING

Words and Music by
Joe Raposo

83
SIDE BY SIDE

Words and Music by
Harry Woods

Moderato

See that sun __ in the morn-ing Peek-ing o - ver the hill, I'll
We're all hunt-ing for some-thing, Some-thing we __ don't know what, 'Cause

bet you're sure __ it al-ways has __ And sure it al - ways will.
none of us __ are sat-is - fied __ With things we know we've got.

That's how I feel a-bout some-one, How some-bo-dy feels a-bout me, We're
We all for-get a-bout moon- light As soon as we've given our vow, But

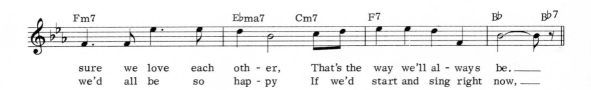

sure we love each oth - er, That's the way we'll al - ways be. ____
we'd all be so hap - py If we'd start and sing right now, ____

Chorus

Oh, we ain't got a bar-rel of mon - ey, May -be we're rag-ged and

fun - ny, But we'll tra-vel a-long __ sing-ing a song __ Side by side.

SOLITAIRE

Words and Music by
Neil Sedaka and Philip Cody

Moderato

There was a man, A lone - ly man
A lit - tle hope goes up in smoke,

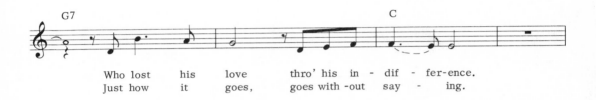

Who lost his love thro' his in - dif - fer-ence.
Just how it goes, goes with -out say - ing.

A heart that cared, that went un - shared
There was a man, a lone - ly man

Un -til it died with -in his si - lence.
Who could com - mand the hand he's play - ing. And

Sol - i - taire's the on-ly game in town, ____ And ev -'ry road that takes him, takes him

85
SOPHISTICATED LADY

Words by Irving Mills and Mitchell Parish
Music by Duke Ellington

86
SUGAR SUGAR

Words and Music by
Jeff Barry and Andy Kim

87
SPINNING WHEEL

Words and Music by
David Clayton Thomas

What goes_up must come_down, Spin-ning Wheel got to go'round._

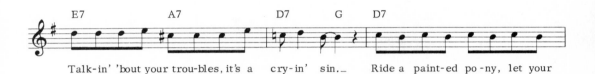

Talk-in' 'bout your trou-bles, it's a cry-in' sin._ Ride a paint-ed po-ny, let your

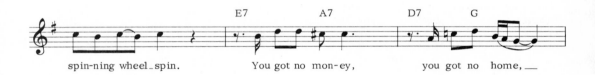

spin-ning wheel_spin. You got no mon-ey, you got no home, __

Spin-ning Wheel all a - lone._ Talk-in' 'bout your trou-bles and you,

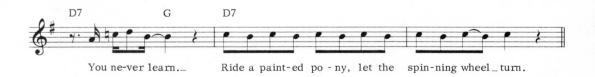

You ne-ver learn._ Ride a paint-ed po - ny, let the spin-ning wheel_ turn.

88
SUPERCALIFRAGILISTICEXPIALIDOCIOUS

Words and Music by
Richard M. Sherman and Robert B. Sherman

Brightly

Um did-dle did-dle did-dle, um did-dle ay! Um did-dle did-dle did-dle,

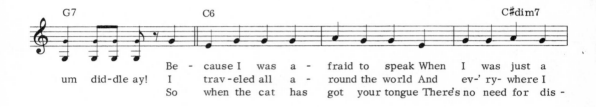

um did-dle ay! I
Be - cause I was a - fraid to speak When I was just a
So when the cat has got your tongue There's no need for dis -

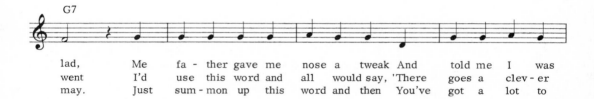

lad, Me fa - ther gave me nose a tweak And told me I was
went I'd use this word and all would say, 'There goes a clev - er
may. Just sum - mon up this word and then You've got a lot to

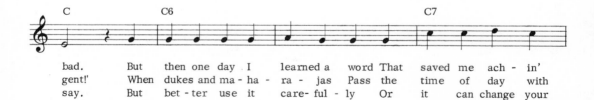

bad. But then one day I learned a word That saved me ach - in'
gent!' When dukes and ma-ha - ra - jas Pass the time of day with
say. But bet - ter use it care- ful - ly Or it can change your

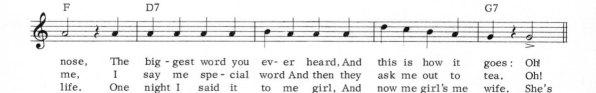

nose, The big - gest word you ev - er heard, And this is how it goes: Oh!
me, I say me spe - cial word And then they ask me out to tea. Oh!
life. One night I said it to me girl, And now me girl's me wife. She's

Chorus

1-2. Su - per - cal - i - frag - il - is - tic - ex - pi - al - i - do - cious!
3. Su - per - cal - i - frag - il - is - tic - ex - pi - al - i - do - cious!

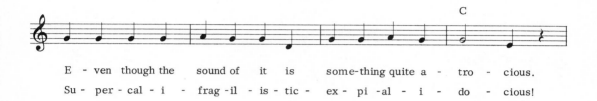

E - ven though the sound of it is some-thing quite a - tro - cious.
Su - per - cal - i - frag -il - is - tic - ex - pi -al - i - do - cious!

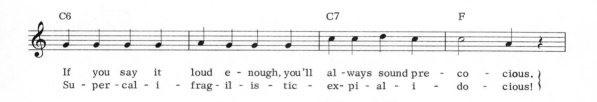

If you say it loud e - nough, you'll al -ways sound pre - co - cious.
Su - per - cal - i - frag -il - is - tic - ex - pi - al - i - do - cious!

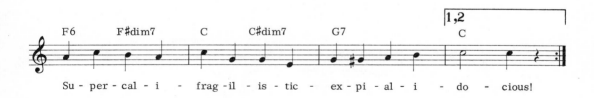

Su - per - cal - i - frag -il - is - tic - ex - pi - al - i - do - cious!

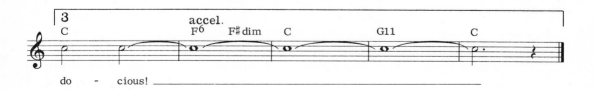

do - cious! _____

89
SUPERSTAR

Words and Music by
Leon Russell and Bonnie Bramlett

THERE GOES MY EVERYTHING

Words and Music by
Dallas Frazier

91
TRY A LITTLE TENDERNESS

Words and Music by
Harry Woods, Jimmy Campbell and Reg Connelly

Moderately slow

She may be wea-ry, Wo-men do get wea-ry Wear-ing the same shab-by

dress, And when she's wea-ry, Try a lit-tle ten-der - ness. ____

You know she's wait-ing, Just an-ti-ci-pa-ting Things she may nev-er pos-sess;

While she's with-out them, Try a lit-tle ten-der - ness. ____ It's

not just sen-ti-men-tal, ____ She has her grief and care, And a

word ____ that's soft and gen-tle Makes it ea-si-er to bear.

You won't re-gret it, Wo-men don't for-get it, Love is their whole hap-pi - ness.

It's all so ea-sy, Try a lit-tle ten-der - ness. ness. ____

TULIPS FROM AMSTERDAM

Words by Neumann and Bader
Music by Ralf Arnie
English lyrics by Gene Martyn

TUXEDO JUNCTION

Words by Buddy Feyne
Music by Erskine Hawkins, William Johnson and Julian Dash

94
WHEN THE SAINTS GO MARCHING IN

New Words and Music
Arrangement by Paul Campbell

WHEN I'M SIXTY-FOUR

Words and Music by
John Lennon and Paul McCartney

Medium tempo

C

When I get old - er, los - ing my hair, __ man - y years from now, __
I could be han - dy mend - ing a fuse __ when your lights have gone; __
Send me a post - card, drop me a line __ stat - ing point of view; __

G7

__ Will you still be send - ing me a Val - en - tine, __
__ You can knit a sweat - er by the fire - side, __
__ In - di - cate pre - cise - ly what you mean to say, __

G   Cdim C#dim G7   C

birth - day greet - ings, bot - tle of wine? __ If I'd been out __ till
Sun - day morn - ings, go for a ride. __ Do - ing the gar - den,
'Yours sin - cere - ly, was - ting a - way.' __ Give me your an - swer,

C7   F

quar - ter to three, __ would you lock the door? ___
dig - ging the weeds. __ Who could ask for more? ___
fill in a form; __ Mine for ev - er - more. ___

[3rd time]

Fm   C   A7   D9,   G13

Will you still need __ me, will you still feed __ me When I'm six - ty -

four?   [top notes] ooh ___
        [2nd time] Ev-'ry sum-mer we can rent a   cot-tage in the Isle of Wight_

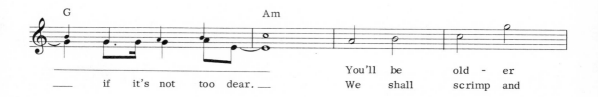

___   if   it's   not   too   dear. __   You'll   be   old - er
                                         We   shall   scrimp   and

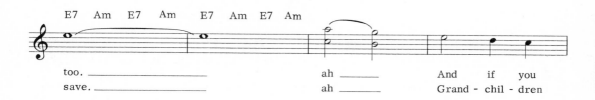

too. _____   ah _____   And   if   you
save. _____   ah _____   Grand - chil - dren

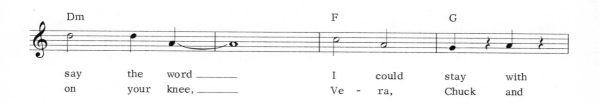

say   the   word _____   I   could   stay   with
on   your   knee, _____   Ve - ra,   Chuck   and

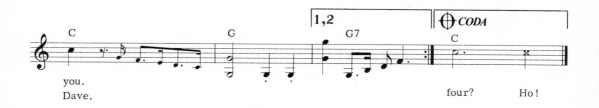

you.   four?   Ho!
Dave.

WITH A LITTLE HELP FROM MY FRIENDS

Words and Music by
John Lennon and Paul McCartney

YOU'RE A STAR

Words and Music by
Tony MacAulay

Moderato

Yes - ter - day __ I was hap-py to play __ for a pen-ny or two __ a song __
signed my name, __ an' the Fri - day came, __ an' the song that I used to sing __

__ Till a fel - la in a black se-dan __ took a shine to my
__ came out on a 'for - ty five' __ a - sing-ing on the

one - man __ band. __ He said, "We got plans for you __
T. V. live. __ As the mus - ic played __ I heard __

__ you'd nev - er dream." __ You're a
__ the peo - ple say, _____

Chorus

star, you're a star; __ a la - mé suit __ and a new gui-tar, __ And I know __

that you'll go far, 'cause you're a star. _____ You're a

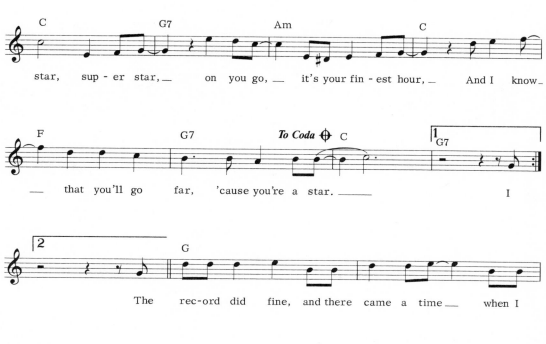

star, sup - er star, __ on you go, __ it's your fin - est hour, __ And I know __

__ that you'll go far, 'cause you're a star. _____ I

The rec-ord did fine, and there came a time __ when I

bought my own __ black se - dan, And a piece of land __ for a

home in St Georg- es Hill. __

3. When I'm low I'm a-happy to go
   To the street where I used to play;
   Even now it makes me laugh
   To have to sign my autograph
   For the folks that used to drop me just a dime;
   (Now they all say,)

   [Chorus]

WHY

Words by Bob Marcucci
Music by Peter De Angelis

YOU ARE MY SUNSHINE

Words and Music by
Jimmie Davis and Charles Mitchel

100
YOU WON'T FIND ANOTHER FOOL LIKE ME

Words and Music by
Geoff Stephens and Tony MacAulay

101
YOU'RE NOBODY 'TIL SOMEBODY LOVES YOU

Words and Music by
Russ Morgan, Larry Stock and James Cavanaugh

101 Hits For Buskers

A series of busking books containing the most asked for songs.
Arranged with melody line, lyrics and chord symbols.

**101 Hits For Buskers
Book 1**
Piano/Organ AM 17229

**101 Hits For Buskers
Book 2**
Piano/Organ AM 19803
B♭ Edition AM 19811

**101 Hits For Buskers
Book 3**
Piano/Organ AM 25099

**101 Hits For Buskers
Book 4**
Piano/Organ AM 26550

**101 Hits For Buskers
Book 5**
Piano/Organ AM 29570

**101 Hits For Buskers
Book 6**
Piano/Organ AM 29869

**101 Hits For Buskers
Book 7**
Piano/Organ AM 33564

Busking For All Occasions
Piano/Organ AM 29596
B♭ Edition AM 29604

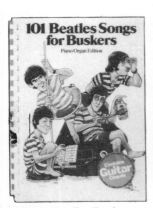

101 Beatles For Buskers
Piano/Organ NO 18392

**101 Country Hits For
Buskers**
Piano/Organ AM 33580

**101 Showtunes For
Buskers**
Piano/Organ AM 32509
B♭ Edition AM 32491

**101 Rock 'n' Roll Hits
For Buskers**
Piano/Organ AM 36484

All Available From Your Local Music Dealer